—*Margaret Mee's Amazon*—

Rain forest, Ecuador.

Margaret Mee's

Amazon

Paintings of plants from Brazilian Amazonia by

Margaret Mee

Text by

Simon Mayo

ROYAL
BOTANIC
GARDENS
KEW

—*Contents*—

—*F o r e w o r d*—

*I*t is a pleasure to write a foreword for anything connected with Margaret Mee, one of the great Amazon explorers of this century. She has combined botany and art to interpret the beauty of the fast disappearing Amazon forest in a way that no other person has been able to capture. It has been an inspiration to know her and watch her courage as she travelled throughout the Amazon Basin. Many times as I have also visited remote places in Amazonia, I have heard stories of this remarkable lady's travels. I am happy that the Royal Botanic Gardens, Kew, can help to celebrate Margaret Mee's more than thirty years of Amazonian work. We do this through this booklet and an exhibition of the sixty paintings that comprise her Amazon collection. It is also a companion to her own recently published book, based on the diaries of her Amazon journeys; **Margaret Mee — in search of flowers of the Amazon Forest** (edited by Tony Morrison, published by Nonesuch Expeditions Ltd., 1988).

I would like to record our deep gratitude to Margaret Mee for granting us permission to exhibit her paintings and for allowing us to reproduce them here. It is also a pleasure to acknowledge the vital collaboration of Antique Collector's Club Ltd. in bringing the paintings to the U.K.

Professor G.T. Prance
Director

—*Biography*—

Margaret Mee

Margaret Mee, one of the most remarkable botanical artists of this century, was born in England on the 22nd May 1909 in Chesham, Buckinghamshire. Although she showed an early interest in art it was not until 1947 that she was able to realize her abilities in this field. After three years at the Camberwell School of Art, where she studied with Victor Pasmore, she and her husband Greville moved to São Paulo, Brazil in 1952. There, like so many European observers before her, she soon became captivated by the luxuriant tropical flora of the forests of the Serra do Mar, the coastal mountains in south-eastern Brazil. Inspired by this wealth of subject material, Margaret, already in her forties, found her true vocation as a botanical artist of exceptional skill, courage and determination. Coastal Brazil soon yielded first place in her affections to the great Amazon Basin and in 1956, only a few years after arriving in Brazil, she made her first journey to search for and paint the plants of the Amazon forests. After working for a while as official artist at the Botanical Institute of São Paulo, she and Greville, also an artist, moved to Rio de Janeiro in 1968. Since then she has devoted herself exclusively to freelance botanical art.

Her fifteen long and arduous journeys to the Amazon forests are described in fascinating detail in her book **Margaret Mee — in search of flowers of the Amazon Forest** (Mee, 1988). Undaunted by the dangers and hardships of travel in the remotest parts of this great wilderness, and constantly renewed by her passionate enthusiasm for plants, she has made extraordinary journeys and discovered unknown species which now bear her name. She has earned the respect and friendship of the leading Amazonian botanists of the day, João Murça Pires, Richard Evans Schultes, William Rodrigues, Ghillean Prance, and many others. Her charisma lies not only in her physical courage and mastery of the technique of botanical art, but in an indomitable spirit, and an unusual empathy with the plants and their mysterious forest world, so resistant to the attentions of anxious scientists, and so easily vanishing with all its treasures before the onslaught of modern human society.

Roberto Burle Marx, the famous Brazilian artist, landscape architect and plantsman, well expresses the essence of her contribution:—

> '...to seek out a plant, bring it from its obscurity and reveal it to those who are inspired by Nature, is a true discovery...' (in Mee, 1968).

Of her artistic gift he writes:—

> 'On examining her work, one has the impression of an achievement made almost without effort. This is only possible when mastery of technique is complete, so clearly true of Margaret, whose work is the reflex of an inner need, carried onto paper with the assurance and judgement of an artist of unrivalled quality.' (in Mee, 1980).

The fruits of her work in Brazil consist of over 400 folio gouache compositions, some fifteen diaries and about 25 sketchbooks packed with detailed drawings and paintings made in the field. Together these comprise an important scientific archive of the Amazon forests and their flora. Not only are her observations meticulous, but the paintings are a truly permanent record of the colours and forms of the plants. Despite the advances of modern photography, there is still no equally stable way to record these qualities for posterity.

Her work is best known through the publication of two magnificent folio books, **Flowers of the Brazilian Forests** (The Tryon Gallery, London, 1968), and **Flores do Amazonas — Flowers of the Amazon** (Record, Rio de Janeiro, 1980). The first arose from an exhibition at the Tryon Gallery in London and brought her work to the notice of a wider public than ever before. The second, sponsored by the Brazilian Government Agency EMBRATUR, was also associated with a London exhibition, promoted by the Brazilian Embassy at the Natural History Museum, and reflects the high esteem in which she is held in her adopted country, Brazil. The preparation of these volumes attracted the enthusiastic collaboration of many botanists but the contribution of Dr Guido F.J. Pabst, the Brazilian orchid specialist, was particularly important.

Her paintings are today distributed throughout the world in private and public collections. Having witnessed over several decades the steady erosion of the forests of the Amazon, Margaret came to feel that her paintings would eventually become important as a record of a natural world that was destined for irrevocable change. Accordingly, she has amassed over the years a special Amazon Collection, which is the subject of this publication. The paintings shown do not include all those she has painted of Amazonian plants, but include some of her finest work. A broad range is shown, from new species discovered by Margaret herself to widespread and characteristic Amazonian plants.

—*A m a z o n i a*—

Stilt roots in the Amazon. Opposite left

*A*mazonia is the vast system of river basins lying east of the Andes mountain chain, which debouche into the Rio Amazonas and eventually into the Atlantic Ocean north of the city of Belém in Brazil. Amazonia occupies most of northern South America and extends for some six million square kilometres, more than half of which falls within Brazilian territory. The rivers can be divided broadly into three kinds. Blackwater rivers drain basins formed from ancient, highly eroded rocks, as in the case of the Rio Negro. Their water is typically dark and peaty-looking, very poor in nutrients, carries very little sediment and is strongly acidic. Clearwater rivers have transparent greenish water and also drain catchments undergoing relatively little erosion. Whitewater rivers are so called

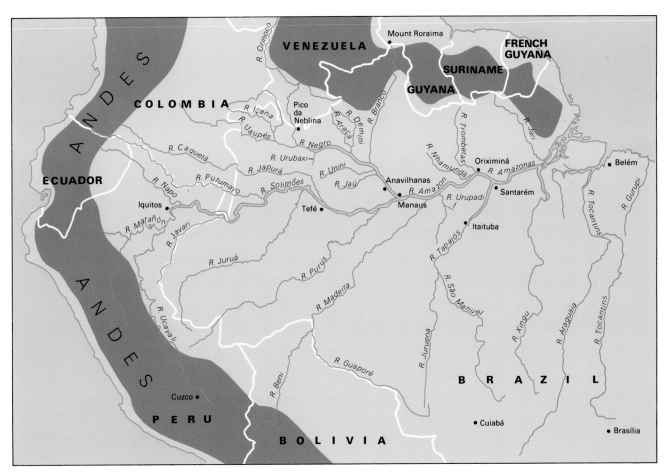

because of the abundant, nutrient-rich sediment they carry; they drain river basins leading down from the geologically young Andes and are only slightly acidic. Besides the rivers themselves, which constitute a fifth of the Earth's total freshwater, Amazonia is made u of a complex of forests, savannas and marshlands and is by far the largest area of primary humid tropical vegetation anywhere in the world. Most of the region is still covered by primary forest (i.e. 'virgin' or 'primaeval', not significantly disturbed by man), but with the onset of major economic and social expansion, the shrinking of the forest area has accelerated significantly in the last 30 years, particularly in Brazil in the south-west (Acre and Rondônia) and ea: (northern Pará).

The scientific exploration and understanding of such a colossal ecological complex is itself an enormous enterprise, and real progress has been made only in recent decades, ironically accelerating in parallel with the change and destruction of the natural habitats. As understanding has grown, so many myths about the Amazon have been exploded. The great stature and extent of Amazonian forest are not the result of rich and fertile soils. Neither are the forests uniform in type, nor have they remained unchanged for many millions of years, reaching back to some early phase of biological evolution, as once was thought.

In fact modern research has shown that Amazonian soils are for the most part very poor and unsuitable for large scale plantation agriculture. The forests are actually a complex mosaic of different types, whose classification is only beginning to be satisfactorily understood. And it has been suggested that as recently as the last Ic Age, much of the Amazon Basin was covered by savannas and open woodlands.

The claim that Amazonia is one of the Earth's greatest treasure-houses of organic diversity has, however, been borne out by moder work - in recent years hundreds of previously unknown species have been discovered for the first time and named. With the growth of awareness in modern times of the practical importance of maintaining species diversity, the significance of Amazonia as one o the world's largest natural gene banks has become increasingly recognized.

A recent advance has been the discovery that many plants and animals show strong concentrations of species diversity in particular parts of the Amazon Basin. Some biologists call these rich zones 'refugia', because it is thought that they may have been preserved as refuges for humid forest which persisted through drier epochs millions of years ago, during the Ice Ages and before, thus preserving species which disappeared elsewhere. As the general climate of Amazonia became more humid again, the forests are thought to have expanded from these refuges, coalesced and taken on the appearance of a continuous and uniform cover.

Whether or not the 'refugium' theory is correct, the discovery of this mosaic of species distributions within Amazonia has vital implications for conservation biology and management. Destruction of 'refuge' areas almost certainly means the extinction of large numbers of species, since so many are not known to grow anywhere else. Conservation of these areas will preserve a much higher proportion of the total species of Amazonia than a randomly chosen series of areas. Using 'refuge' science as a strategic basis, the Brazilian Government has in recent years created a number of important new Amazonian national parks.

Other factors are also important in understanding the forest. The biological interdependency of many forest species is such that to determine the minimum viable area for a rainforest reserve is a very difficult task. Unless the area is big enough to allow a high proportion of the biological links to remain intact, the forest reserve will, over time, become impoverished as species die out. This can be viewed as a sort of 'genetic erosion' of forest reserves. The need is to discover the minimum area required to maintain the species indefinitely.

During the last 35 years, Margaret Mee has watched the threats to the Amazonian forests steadily grow, with all that this implies for the plant life. Her Amazon journeys have coincided with the most important industrial, economic and demographic changes in the history of Amazonian countries, and especially in Brazil. Even as late as the Fifties, cities like Manaus and Belém were small and undeveloped in comparison with today. Large areas of the Amazon Basin, such as northern Mato Grosso, had scarcely been explored and there were virtually no roads linking the major towns with each other or with the populous south and east of the country. Her experience, set forth in her diaries and paintings, is an outstanding and unusual record of this momentous period in Amazonian history.

The Margaret Mee
—Amazon Trust—

*I*t has long been Margaret Mee's hope that a suitable home woul eventually be found where the Amazon Collection paintings shown here, together with her original notebooks, sketchbooks and diaries, could be permanently housed and made available for the benefit of present and future generations.

To bring this about, a group of friends and colleagues have recently formed the **Margaret Mee Amazon Trust**, dedicated to the task of raising funds to ensure the preservation of Margaret's unique Amazon Collection for posterity, to the fostering of awareness of the Amazon forests and their plant life and to promoting continuance o artistic and botanical work in Amazonia in the spirit of Margaret's researches.

Further information about the Margaret Mee Amazon Trust can be obtained from:— **The Margaret Mee Amazon Trust, c/o Dr S.J. Mayo, Herbarium, Royal Botanic Gardens, Kew, Richmond, Surrey, TW9 3AE, U.K.**

The
—Amazon Collection—

*T*he 60 paintings are gouache on paper and are of plants seen and collected in Brazilian Amazonia. Her working method starts with detailed sketches of the plant in the forest, with colour notes and records of locality and habitat, followed by the collection of living individuals whenever possible. The 25 sketchbooks, started in 1958, are an important record of Amazonian life. The plants are sent or brought back to Rio de Janeiro where the paintings are worked up as finished compositions in her studio. This procedure is reflected in the choice of plants painted. Plant groups like orchids and bromeliads are favoured, since they can be more readily collected and flowered in cultivation. As a result, the field notes and sketches can later be complemented directly as her plants come into flower.

Gustavia pulchra
Amazonas

— Margaret Mee

1. GUSTAVIA PULCHRA (family Lecythidaceae) Opposite left

Painting completed in 1979, published in Mee (1980); plant from the Rio Negro.

This very beautiful species has a fairly restricted distribution being confined to the upper Rio Negro and crossing the border into neighbouring Venezuela. The flowers are borne below the leaves, springing directly from the branches; this is quite common in rainforest trees and is known as cauliflory. Like many Amazonian plants, it was first discovered by the English botanist Richard Spruce during his epic botanical explorations of Amazonia and the Andes between 1849 and 1864.

2. COUROUPITA SUBSESSILIS (family Lecythidaceae) Right

Painting completed in 1984; plant from the Paraná Yamundá, a tributary of the Rio Trombetas, Pará.

This is the cannonball tree genus, so named after its globose fruits which at maturity fall to the ground. It is thought that wild pig feed on the evil-smelling pulp in which the seeds are enveloped and thus disperse them. The genus exhibits cauliflory in a spectacular fashion, the trunk of older trees becoming covered in a tangle of projecting flowering branches bearing fleshy flowers and massive fruit.

3. SYMPHONIA GLOBULIFERA (family Clusiaceae) Far right

Painting completed in October 1985; plant from the Paraná Yamundá, a tributary of the Rio Trombetas.

*The genus **Symphonia** occurs in both tropical Africa and tropical America, but in the Americas only this single widespread species is found, occurring in various forest types. It is a medium-sized to large tree reaching 35 metres in height. The tissues are full of bright yellow juice, which flows abundantly when the twigs or bark are cut and has many medicinal uses by the Amazon Indians.*

TREES

Trees are the essence of Amazonia, forming the basic substance of the forest and its architecture. They strongly influence the regional climate by maintaining constant humidity, and provide support and sustenance for hundreds of thousands of animals and plants. Most of the life-sustaining nutrients of Amazonia are held not in the soil but in the tissues of the trees, which is one reason why loss of trees is so damaging to the ecosystem. Another is that the forest and its trees protect the soil from erosion, which can be very destructive because of the violence of the rain and the physical nature of the soil. Last but not least, the trees together form a vast buffer, a sponge which absorbs water and releases it again more gradually into the river system. This stabilizes the effects of flood and drought and maintains the river system itself in a more constant condition. Combined, these various components form a huge stable matrix composed of trees and water in which uncountable numbers of organisms have found a living during the course of evolution.

The lecythids (Lecythidaceae) are one of Amazonia's important tree groups, and include the famous brazil nut tree (*Bertholletia excelsa*). This is one of the tallest and grandest of the rainforest trees, besides being one of the most useful — in Brazil it is known as the 'Pará Chestnut' (Castanha do Pará).

4. *UNKNOWN PLANT* Above

Painting completed in 1972, published in Mee (1980); plant from the Rio Urubaxi, Amazonas.

   *This plant has so far defied attempts by botanists to place it even in a family. Little more can be done until it has been recollected in flower. The earlier identification as '***Ochna** sp.***' does not seem to be correct.*

5. *HETEROSTEMON MIMOSOIDES* (*family Leguminosae*) Above right

Painting completed in 1978, published in Mee (1980); plant from the Rio Cuieiras, a left bank tributary of the Rio Negro near Manaus, Amazonas.

   Heterostemon *is a small genus concentrated in the Rio Negro river basin and neighbouring parts of Colombia and Venezuela.* **Heterostemon mimosoides** *is a low shrub or small tree characteristic of igapó and várzea forests (permanent and seasonal swamp forest respectively). Margaret's painting of another species,* **H. ellipticus**, *was published in her book* **Flowers of the Brazilian Forests** (*1968*).

6. *GUSTAVIA AUGUSTA* (*family Lecythidaceae*) Opposite right

Painting completed in November 198? plant from the Rio Amazonas.

   This is a medium-sized tree to some 20 metres in height and is a common plant along river margins and widespread throughout the Guianas and Amazonia; the seeds may be dispersed by water. The old, hemispherical fruit remains can be seen hanging from branches in the background; also shown are a white egret, the hanging nests of the 'oropendula' bird, epiphytic aroids, orchids, and bromeliads and a **Mauritia** *palm.*

Gustavia augusta
amazonas Nov 1985

Margaret Mee

Memora schombergia "De Candolle"
Meirs
Orisciminci, Pará

Margaret Mee
June. 1984

LIANAS AND HEMIPARASITES

Lianas are woody climbing plants and form a characteristic and important element in tropical rainforests. Richard Spruce described them memorably:-

> 'Of all lianas…the most fantastic are the Yabotím-mitá-mitá or Land-turtle's ladders [*Bauhinia* – Leguminosae], which have compressed, ribbon-like stems, wavy as if they had been moulded out of paste, and while still soft indented at every few inches by pressing in the fist….The great majority of lianas, however, have more or less rounded stems; and there is scarcely any family of plants which does not include some members who get up in the world by scrambling upon their more robust and self-standing neighbours. Where two or more of these vagabonds come into collision in mid-air, and find nothing else to twine upon, they twine around each other as closely as the strands of a cable, and the stronger of them generally ends by squeezing the life out of the weaker'.

8. PSITTACANTHUS CINCTUS (*family Loranthaceae*) *Above*

Painting completed in 1982; plant from the Rio Negro, Amazonas.

The known range of this species extends along the Rio Negro from Manaus in Brazil to the Amazonian territory of neighbouring Venezuela. The bulging upturned tips to the flowers are characteristic. Richard Spruce collected it on lecythid trees (brazil nut family) around Manaus, known in the 1850s as Barra do Rio Negro.

The bignones (Bignoniaceae) include many very beautiful lianas such as the commonly cultivated trumpet creeper (*Campsis*). The flowers of this family tend to be conspicuous and trumpet-shaped, and their leaves are usually subdivided pinnately, like those of an ash tree.

In hemiparasites the dependence of one plant on another becomes more complete. The loranths (Loranthaceae), a family of mistletoes, are a group of woody plants which have a parasitic attachment to their host tree. However, being also green and photosynthetic, they can synthesize sugars using sunlight and are therefore not entirely dependent on their hosts. Their undistinguished lifestyle is belied by very showy and often beautiful flowers, as in *Psittacanthus*.

9. PHRYGANOCYDIA CORYMBOSA (*family Bignoniaceae*) *Left*

Painting completed in 1985; plant from the Paraná Yamundá, Pará.
The flowers of this widespread tropical American liana are usually rose, lilac or magenta, but in some places white-flowered plants are found. Margaret's plant comes from near the mouth of the Rio Trombetas, not far from where Spruce also collected it 130 years before, at Santarém.

7. MEMORA SCHOMBURGKII (*family Bignoniaceae*) *Opposite left*

Painting completed in 1984; plant from Oriximiná, Pará.
This species occurs in the Guianas and Amazonia. The fruit, as in many other bignones, are long, pendulous pods, at first sight much like those of legumes. Oriximiná lies near the mouth of the Rio Trombetas, one of the largest northern tributaries in lower Amazonia.

Margaret Mee 1982

Clusia grandifolia Endl.
Rio Negro, Amazonas

20

10. *CLUSIA GRANDIFOLIA* (*family Clusiaceae*) *Opposite left*

Painting completed in 1983; plant from the Rio Negro, Amazonas.

Another species first discovered by the indefatigable Spruce. He found it in 1852 at Panuré on the Rio Uaupés, a tributary of the Negro in igapó forest. It is also known from neighbouring regions of Venezuela, but it has been collected only infrequently.

STRANGLERS

The stranglers, from their sinister life-style, are a well-known type of rain-forest plant. The genus *Clusia* is typical; the seedlings and juveniles begin life as epiphytes (see below) on a host tree. After some while their roots reach the ground, and thereafter expand and join laterally until they form their own self-supporting stilt root system, or even an entire hollow trunk. The enclosed host tree eventually succumbs, mainly due to its crown being suppressed by that of the more vigorous strangler. This habit is also common in figs (*Ficus* – family Moraceae).

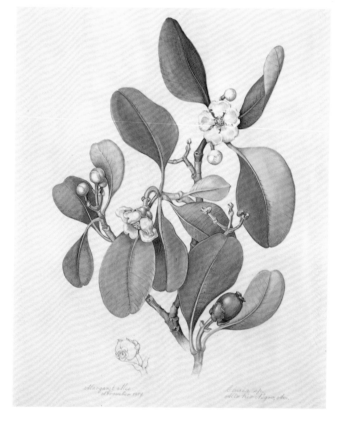

11. *CLUSIA NEMOROSA* (*family Clusiaceae*) *Above*

Painting completed in 1973, published in Mee (1980); plant from the Rio Araçá, Amazonas.

Clusia nemorosa is a good deal more widespread and hence better known than **C. grandifolia***. Geographically it exhibits an interesting feature, being one of a large number*

of plant species to occur both in Amazonia and in eastern Brazil but not in the seasonally dry region in between. In the east it occurs in the coastal forest zone known as the 'Mata Atlântica'.

12. *CLUSIA* sp. (*possibly* **C. grandiflora**, *family Clusiaceae*) *Above right*

Painting completed in November 1987;

plant from the upper Rio Negro, Amazonas.

Like **C. grandifolia**, **C. grandiflora** *has a somewhat restricted range, but differs in having an eastern Amazonian distribution. It is known from Guyana and Surinam, and from the region of Belém in Pará, Brazil.*

Margaret Mee
July, 1981

Heliconia adeleana L.Em.
Amazonas

22

FOREST FLOOR HERBS

13. HELICONIA *unnamed species* (*family Heliconiaceae*) *Opposite left*

Painting completed in 1981; plant from the Rio Amazonas.

In tall, primary lowland rainforests much of the forest floor is dark and with only a relatively sparse covering of herbs adapted to cope with the lack of light. Some of our most successful house plants come from this kind of habitat (e.g. the juvenile form of *Philodendron scandens* – family Araceae, known as the sweetheart vine). But wherever a tree has fallen to create a clearing or the forest meets a river margin, the higher light intensity results in vigorous herbaceous growth. Among such robust, fast-growing herbs are the heliconias. Like the bananas, to which they are related, they may reach huge sizes, but their characteristic and elegant flowering shoots give them a beauty all their own. The flowers themselves are small and borne within the large, often brightly coloured bracts (modified leaves), whose shapes form an arresting ensemble. In many species the inflorescences hang down, but in others they may be erect. The remarkable and conspicuous inflorescences of these plants are the result of adaptation to pollination by birds. Like man, birds have keen sight, and bird-pollinated flowers tend to rely on strong visual signals for attraction.

Despite their striking forms, these plants have been very poorly known until recently. Large numbers of new species have been discovered in the last ten years but, like two of those shown here, many remain to be named.

14. HELICONIA CHARTACEA (*family Heliconiaceae*) *Right*

Painting completed in 1975, published in Mee (1980); from a cultivated plant.
This species occurs in western Amazonia and was described only in 1972. Margaret's painting is from a plant in the gardens of Roberto Burle Marx, who has an outstanding collection of the genus.

15. HELICONIA *unnamed species* (*family Heliconiaceae*) *Far right*

Painting undated; plant from the Rio Uaupés.

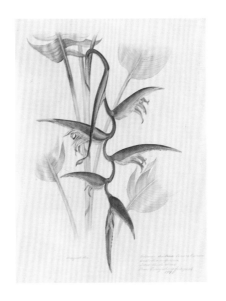

Margaret Mee
August 1978

Nymphea rudgeana by E.W. Meyer
Urucará, Lower Amazon

16. NYMPHAEA RUDGEANA (family Nymphaeaceae) Opposite left

Painting completed in 1978, published in Mee (1980); plant from the region of Urucará, Rio Amazonas, Amazonas.

*A smaller relative of **Victoria**, this waterlily is known from the Guianas, Venezuela and Brazilian Amazonia. Like the cactus **Selenicereus wittii**, the flowers open after nightfall, but are pollinated by beetles rather than hawkmoths. The species was first discovered in 1849 by Richard Spruce at Óbidos, on the Rio Amazonas near Santarém.*

WATER PLANTS AND AROIDS

In a region where water plays such a dominant part in the ecosystem, it is not surprising that extraordinary water plants are to be found. The giant waterlily, *Victoria amazonica*, is probably the most famous Amazonian plant of all, and since the last century has remained a coveted show-plant of botanic gardens.

The aroids, or Araceae, also include many aquatic plants; some are of huge size, like the 'aninga' (*Montrichardia arborescens*) which grows in dense populations along the river margins of Amazonia. Other well-known aroid genera found there are *Philodendron* and *Monstera*. These include climbers, epiphytes and hemiepiphytes. The latter start life as climbing plants rooted in the ground but eventually lose contact by rotting of the old stem. Connection with the ground is later reestablished by means of long hanging roots, which can be very stout, resembling cables.

*17. **PHILODENDRON ARCUATUM** (family Araceae) Right*

Painting completed in 1977, published in Mee (1980); plant from near Manaus, Amazonas.

Not a well-known species, though quite widespread – collections have been made throughout western Amazonia, including Bolivia, and the Guianas. The stems are covered by a dense layer of coarse hairs, an odd character that crops up in other species. Margaret's painting is the only colour illustration known.

*18. **UROSPATHA SAGITTIFOLIA** (family Araceae) Far right*

Painting completed in 1976, published in Mee (1980); plant from near Manaus, Amazonas.

*A swamp-dwelling aroid found throughout the Guianas, most of Amazonia, and reaching as far east as Bahia. The curious erect and twisted shape of the floral bract is also found in some species of a related genus **Cyrtosperma** from south-east Asia, testifying to ancient connections between the plants of the Old and New Worlds.*

19. *STREPTOCALYX POEPPIGII*
(*family Bromeliaceae*) *Opposite left*

*Painting completed in 1985; plant
from the Rio Trombetas, Pará.*

*A widespread Amazonian species
first collected by, and named after
Eduard Poeppig, an outstanding
German botanist and explorer who
made an important early journey to the
upper Amazon of Peru and Brazil; his
plant came from Tefé on the Solimões.*

TRUE EPIPHYTES

True epiphytes have no connection with the ground throughout
their life cycle. The rainforest trees offer a variety of habitats for
epiphytes. Those that can tolerate greater shade, but require more
constant humidity throughout the day tend to prefer the trunks and
major boughs. More resistant epiphytes are found higher in the
canopy, where they profit from unlimited light, but are exposed to
fierce oscillations of humidity between day and night. Paradoxically,
in this habitat such plants have developed adaptations, such as
succulence, which recall those of some desert plants; for both water
stress is an important factor. Nevertheless, the presence of numerous
epiphytes in a forest is a clear sign of a climate which is very humid
throughout the year. Most epiphytic flowering plants cannot survive
long dry periods. Their adaptations are sufficient only to tide them
through the daily period of relative drought caused in the forest
canopy by the sun. In less humid forests, and in transitional zones
between rainforest and drier vegetation, it is common to find
normally epiphytic species growing on the ground or on rocks,
wherever the humidity is greater.

Bromeliads (family Bromeliaceae) and orchids (family
Orchidaceae) both belong to the monocotyledons, that great class of
plants that includes the cereals, the palms and the lilies. Both
bromeliads and orchids include very large numbers of epiphytes,
and exhibit remarkable adaptations connected with this way of life.

20. *STREPTOCALYX LONGIFOLIUS*
(*family Bromeliaceae*) *Right*

*Painting completed in 1982; plant
from the Rio Negro.*

*First discovered by the French
botanist Joseph Martin in French
Guiana. His collections, the fruit of
years of dedicated labour, eventually
ended up in Britain when the ship
carrying them back to France was
captured by English privateers in 1803.*

21. *VRIESIA HELICONIOIDES* (*family
Bromeliaceae*) *Far right*

*Painting completed in 1973; plant
from the Rio Demini, Amazonas.*

Margaret Mee
1976

Aechmea tillandsioides (Mart. ex. Schult)
Amazonas, Rio Negro

22. AECHMEA TILLANDSIOIDES
(*family Bromeliaceae*) *Opposite left*

Painting completed in 1976, published in Mee (1980); plant from the Rio Negro, Amazonas.
A widespread species occurring from Mexico to south-western Amazonia.

23. AECHMEA POLYANTHA (*family Bromeliaceae*) *Below*

Painting completed in 1973, published in Mee (1980); plant from the Rio Maraú, near Maués, Amazonas.
First discovered by Margaret in 1972, in igapó forest (permanent swamp forest), and first described botanically in 1974.

THE BROMELIADS: Margaret Mee has had a long acquaintance with bromeliads; they are a group in which she has taken a particular interest since her earlier years in Brazil when she worked at the Instituto de Botânica of São Paulo on the preparation of a large series of paintings illustrating bromeliads of the whole of Brazil. This was carried out in collaboration with the American botanist Lyman B. Smith, the pre-eminent authority on the botany of bromeliads.

Margaret's knowledge of this group has helped her to discover in Amazonia a number of previously unknown species, such as *Aechmea polyantha* and *A. meeana*, which remain scientifically known only from Margaret's collections. These rarities were discovered not much more than 150 miles from Manaus, which demonstrates that the flora remains generally poorly known.

24. AECHMEA MEEANA (*family Bromeliaceae*) *Above*

Painting completed in 1978, published in Mee (1980); plant from the Rio Maraú, near Maués, Amazonas.
In the traditional manner, this species was named by Lyman Smith in honour of Margaret as the discoverer of the plant.

26. AECHMEA TOCANTINA (*family Bromeliaceae*) *Above*

Painting completed in 1981; plant from the Rio Nhamundá, Pará.
   Widespread in South America, A. **tocantina** *was first discovered by the English-born botanist Hugh Weddell on the Rio Tocantins, the easternmost major river of southern Amazonia.*

25. AECHMEA RODRIGUESIANA (*family Bromeliaceae*) *Opposite left*

Painting completed in 1977, published in Mee (1980); plant from the Rio Maraú, near Maués, Amazonas.
   Named after William A. Rodrigues, the Brazilian botanist who first discovered it. The painting also shows a young **Clusia** *epiphyte and in the background, the strange leaves of the aroid* **Philodendron goeldii**, *reminiscent of those of hellebores.*

27. AECHMEA HUEBNERI (*family Bromeliaceae*) *Above*

Painting completed in 1977, published in Mee (1980); plant from the Rio Nhamundá, Pará.
   This species has the interesting geographical distribution, previously noted in **Clusia nemorosa**, *which jumps from Amazonia to the east coast of Brazil.*

Margaret
Mee
May, 1949

Neoregelia margaretae L. th. Smith
Col. Amazonas, Rio Icana
Cult. Sitio Burle Marc

32

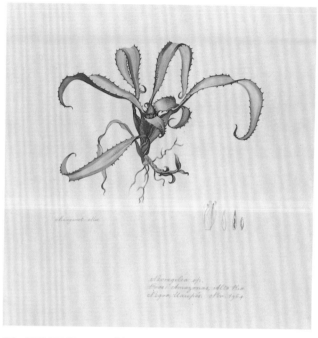

30. NEOREGELIA sp. (*family Bromeliaceae*) *Above*

Painting completed 1965; plant from the Rio Uaupés, Amazonas.

29. NEOREGELIA LEVIANA (*family Bromeliaceae*) *Above*

Painting completed in 1968; plant from the Rio Negro, Amazonas.

*Like **N. margaretae**, this species is known only from Margaret's collection, which was made on the Rio Cauaburi in 1967. The Cauaburi is a left bank tributary of the Negro and leads to the base of the famous Pico da Neblina mountain on the border with Venezuela.*

The painting itself is dated December 1964. This conflicts with the dates of collection given here and in the original publication of the species.

The genus *Neoregelia*, like *Aechmea*, is well known in cultivation. Unlike *Aechmea*, however, which bears its flowers on a stalk, *Neoregelia* has a very contracted inflorescence, with the flowers crowded into a sunken 'nest' at the centre of the leaf rosette. An especially attractive feature of many species is the brightly coloured ruff of inner leaves. The majority of the 70 or so species of the genus grow in eastern Brazil, mostly in the 'Mata Atlântica' coastal forest zone, which in former days was a veritable treasure house of ornamental bromeliads. The 12 remaining species form a distinct group found only in Amazonia. Margaret has collected four of the five species known from Amazonian Brazil and first discovered three of them herself, *N. margaretae* L.B. Smith, *N. leviana* L.B. Smith and *N. meeana* Reitz. Her work on *Neoregelia* thus amounts to a major scientific contribution to knowledge of the genus.

28. NEOREGELIA MARGARETAE (*family Bromeliaceae*) *Opposite left*

Painting completed in 1979; plant from the Rio Içana, Amazonas.

The Rio Içana is a tributary on the right bank of the upper Rio Negro,

beyond the Uaupés. In this remote region Margaret discovered **N. margaretae** *in January 1965; it has not yet been recollected.*

31. NEOREGELIA ELEUTHEROPETALA
(*family Bromeliaceae*) Left

Painting completed in 1971, published in Mee (1980); plant from the Rio Urupadi, Amazonas/Pará.

This is the most widespread of the Amazonian neoregelias, and is known from Amazonian regions of Colombia, Venezuela, Peru and Brazil. The Rio Urupadi lies between the Tapajós and the Amazonas, and runs across the border between the states of Amazonas and Pará.

32. BILLBERGIA DECORA (*family Bromeliaceae*) Opposite right

Painting completed in 1979, published in Mee (1980); plant from the Arquipelago das Anavilhanas, Rio Negro, Amazonas.

Billbergia has relatively few species in Amazonia. This one had not been recorded from the Rio Negro region until Margaret found it in the Anavilhanas, a complex of river islands just north of Manaus on the Negro.

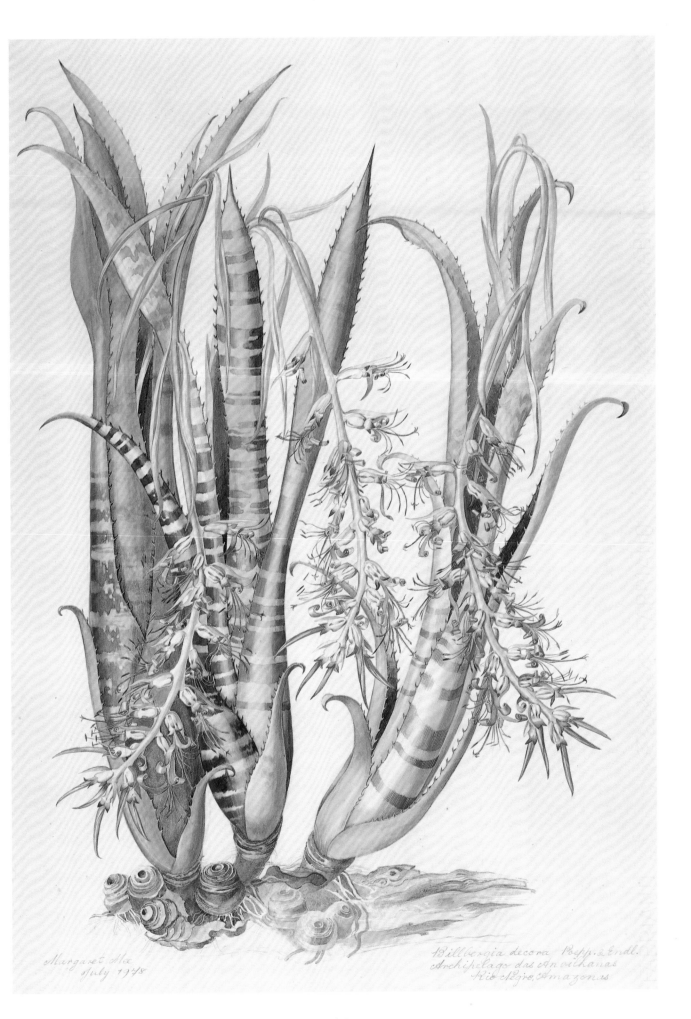

Margaret Mee
July 1948

Billbergia decora Popp. a Endl.
Archipelago das Anoilhanas
Rio Negro, Amazonas

*Strophocactus
wittei
Tarivilcanhas, Amazonas*

*Margaret Mee
February, 1978*

33. SELENICEREUS WITTII (*family Cactaceae*) *Opposite left*

Painting completed in 1978, published in Mee (1980); plant from the Arquipelago das Anavilhanas, Rio Negro, Amazonas.

This, her earliest picture of the species, is of plants with developing fruit.

34. SELENICEREUS WITTII (*family Cactaceae*) *Right*

Painting completed in 1981; plant from the Arquipelago das Anavilhanas, Rio Negro, Amazonas.

In this later painting Margaret was able to find plants which had flowered the previous night; already the flowers are withering.

A NIGHT-FLOWERING CACTUS: The story of Margaret's pursuit of the curious epiphytic cactus *Selenicereus wittii* is told in full in her recently published book (Mee, 1988). The plant was previously known as *Strophocactus wittii*, but recently cactus experts have agreed that the genus *Strophocactus* cannot be kept distinct from the better-known *Selenicereus*, which includes the 'Queen of the Night', *S. grandiflorus*.

Selenicereus wittii grows in the igapó, or permanently flooded swamp forest. Like some other kinds of epiphytic cacti, the stems are flattened so that they resemble leaves. Each flower has the form of a very long tube which splays out rather abruptly at the tip. This shape, combined with the night-flowering habit, suggests that pollination is by long-tongued hawkmoths, which are known to pollinate other species of the genus.

Margaret Mee

Rudolfiella aurantiaca (Lindl.) Hoehne
Rio Negro, Amazonas
November 1971

35. RUDOLFIELLA AURANTIACA
(family Orchidaceae) Opposite left

Painting completed in 1971, published in Mee (1980); plant from the Rio Cuieiras, right bank tributary of the Rio Negro, Amazonas.

*The plant is painted as Margaret found it, on a Jará palm (**Leopoldinia pulchra**), a common habitat for this orchid in the igapó forests of the Negro basin. It is widespread elsewhere in Amazonia and the Guianas.*

THE ORCHIDS: The orchids are another group of plants to which Margaret has devoted much time and effort over the years. This is not surprising in that they are plants of abiding fascination and richly represented in Brazil, which is known to harbour some 2300 species in 191 genera. But beyond these general considerations, her interest was stimulated and fostered by her friendship with the Brazilian orchid specialist, Guido F.J. Pabst, a remarkable man, whose death in 1980 robbed Brazilian botany of one of its outstanding figures. His crowning achievement is the two volume **Orchidaceae Brasilienses**, written in collaboration with F. Dungs and published between 1975 and 1977. The dustjackets of both volumes are adorned with paintings by Margaret (*Coryanthes albertinae* — Vol. 1; *Rudolfiella aurantiaca* — Vol. 2). In turn, Guido Pabst took charge of the preparation of the scientific descriptions of her second folio book, **Flores do Amazonas — Flowers of the Amazon**. In his professional life, Guido Pabst was a senior executive of VARIG, the national airline, a position which made heavy demands. But his energy and enthusiasm were such that in his spare time he founded and ran the Herbarium Bradeanum, an important private botanical institute in Rio, with its house journal **Bradea**. The Herbarium was in Pabst's day situated in a delightful house in the neighbourhood of Santa Teresa, just down the hill from Margaret's house. Here was an agreeable place where Margaret could talk over her latest finds of orchids and bromeliads with Pabst and Edmundo Pereira, the bromeliad specialist, the three of them linked by a love of plants and decades of experience in the wilds of Brazil in search of 'vegetable prizes'.

36. ONCIDIUM LANCEANUM (family Orchidaceae) Right

Painting completed in 1975, published in Mee (1980); plant from the upper Rio Negro, Amazonas.

Oncidium is a large genus of orchids and is widely cultivated. This striking species is found in the Guianas, Venezuela, Trinidad and Amazonas state in Brazil, and is named after John H. Lance, who brought it into cultivation from Surinam.

37. ONCIDIUM sp. (family Orchidaceae) Far right

Painting completed in 1985; plant from Amazonas state.

Margaret Mee
1977

Catasetum saccatum Lindl.

Amazonas

40

38. CATASETUM SACCATUM (*family Orchidaceae*) *Opposite left*

Painting completed in 1977, published in Mee (1980); plant from Rio Demini, left bank tributary of the Rio Negro, Amazonas.
Note the green female flowers and the more numerous maroon male ones.

The genus *Catasetum* has caused botanists many problems over the years. These have arisen mainly from the fact that the flowers are unisexual and the female and male flowers look rather different. As a result, the herbarium collections which have traditionally been the basis for taxonomic work give a confusing picture of the real situation. Without careful studies in the forest or in cultivation, it is not always possible to associate unequivocally two forms as the different sexes of the same species. The problem is made worse when working from pressed herbarium specimens, which in orchids give a poor idea of the flower structure. Herein lies one of the significant scientific merits of Margaret's paintings.

39. CATASETUM BARBATUM (*family Orchidaceae*) *Left*

Painting completed in 1975, published in Mee (1980); plant from the Rio Unini, a right bank tributary of the Rio Negro, Amazonas.

40. CATASETUM APPENDICULATUM (*family Orchidaceae*) *Above*

Painting completed in 1985; plant from the Rio Negro, Amazonas.

41. *CATASETUM MACROCARPUM*
(*family Orchidaceae*) *Above*

*Painting completed in August 1981;
plant from Amazonas state.
    Plant with male flowers.*

42. *CATASETUM MACROCARPUM*
(*family Orchidaceae*) *Above*

*Painting completed in July 1981; plant
from Amazonas state.
    Plants with female flowers.*

44. *CATASETUM FIMBRIATUM*
(*family Orchidaceae*) *Above*

Painting completed in 1982; plant from the upper Rio Juruena, Mato Grosso.

43. *CATASETUM GALERITUM* (*family Orchidaceae*) *Above*

Painting completed in August 1981; plant from Amazonas state.

45. CATASETUM PUNCTATUM (*family Orchidaceae*) *Right*

Painting completed in 1974, published in Mee (1980); plant from the Rio Mamori, near Manaus, Amazonas.

46. CATASETUM sp. (*family Orchidaceae*) *Below*

Painting completed in 1972; plant from the Rio Negro, Amazonas.

47. CATASETUM DISCOLOR (*family Orchidaceae*) *Left*

Painting completed in July 1981; plant from the Rio Maraú near Maués, Amazonas.

48. IONOPSIS UTRICULARIOIDES (*family Orchidaceae*) *Opposite right*

Painting completed in August 1984; plant from Rio Cumina-mirim, Pará.
*   This very elegant orchid is related to* **Oncidium**, *and has been known to botanists since the eighteenth century. Though very widespread, even reaching as far as Florida, it is not known from western Amazonia.*

Ionopsis utricularioides (Sw.) Lindl.
Rio Buiuina-Mirim, Pará

Margaret Mee
August, 1984

Sobralia margaretae Pabst
Rio Urupadi, Amazonas
1947

Margaret Mee

50. ZYGOSEPALUM LABIOSUM
(*family Orchidaceae*) *Above*

*Painting completed in 1976; plant
from Pará state.*

Zygosepalum, not to be confused
with the better known *Zygopetalum*, is
a small genus of orchids which in
Brazil occurs mostly in western
Amazonia; **Z. labiosum** is more
widespread. The painting shows the
swollen stems which help the plant to
withstand water stress during the hottest
part of the day.

51. GONGORA MACULATA (*family*
Orchidaceae) *Above*

*Painting completed in February 1959;
plant from the Rio Gurupi,
Pará/Maranhão.*

This species has also been known as
G. quinquenervis *Ruiz & Pavon. The
painting is from her first journey to
Amazonia, and the locality is at the
extreme eastern edge of the Amazon
basin; the Rio Gurupi marks the border
between the states of Maranhão and
Pará.*

49. SOBRALIA MARGARITAE (*family*
Orchidaceae) *Opposite left*

*Painting completed in 1977, published
in Mee (1980); plant from the Rio
Urupadi, Amazonas/Pará.*

This very fine epiphyte is another of
Margaret's discoveries, and was named
in her honour by her friend Guido
Pabst. The genus **Sobralia** has very
attractive foliage, in contrast to many
orchids, and the reedy stems are
characteristic.

52. *COCHLEANTHES AMAZONICA* (*family Orchidaceae*) *Above left*

Painting completed in September 1978; plant from Amazonas state.

This is not a well-known species, and from the little information available its distribution seems quite restricted, with records from the Rio Marañón in Peru and in western Amazonas in Brazil. No specimens exist at Kew.

53. *ENCYCLIA RANDII* (*family Orchidaceae*) *Above right*

Painting completed in 1983; plant from Amazonas state.

A Brazilian species which extends from western Amazonas to the eastern state of Pernambuco. It was discovered in the last century by Edward Rand near Tefé on the Rio Solimões and named by the renowned Brazilian botanist João Barbosa Rodrigues.

54. *CATTLEYA VIOLACEA* (*family Orchidaceae*) *Opposite right*

Painting completed in 1981; plant from the Rio Cuiuni, right bank tributary of the Rio Negro, Amazonas.

***Cattleya violacea** was first discovered during the celebrated journey of Alexander von Humboldt and Aimé Bonpland to the Americas between 1799 and 1804; they found it on the Rio Orinoco in Venezuela. Margaret's painting is full of botanical detail of the igapó forest; there is an epiphytic **Clusia** in the foreground and the aquatic aroid **Urospatha sagittifolia** in the lower right hand corner. Fruiting plants of the epiphytic cactus **Rhipsalis** dangle from the same trunk which bears the orchid. On the left, lecythid fruit can be seen high up, and down below a clump of **Heliconia** plants are pushing forth new inflorescences.*

Margaret Mee
1981

Cattleya violacea
Rio Curini, Amazonas

49

Margaret Mee
September, 1975

Mormodes amazonicum L.Dl.
Urucará, Amazonas

55. *MORMODES BUCCINATOR*
(*family Orchidaceae*) *Opposite left*

Painting completed in September 1975, published in Mee (1980); plant from Rio Macacaua, Urucará, Amazonas.

In the genus *Mormodes*, as in its relative *Catasetum*, the flowers may vary considerably in shape within a single species, and may be unisexual. Darwin studied their curious pollination mechanisms more than 120 years ago. The species shown here was previously known as *Mormodes amazonicum*.

56. *MORMODES BUCCINATOR*
(*family Orchidaceae*) *Above*

Painting completed in 1985; plant from Amazonas state.

57. *CLOWESIA WARCZEWITZII*
(*family Orchidaceae*) *Above*

Painting completed in April 1971; plant from the Rio Araçá, a tributary of the Negro, Amazonas.

*Although small in number of species, the genus **Clowesia** stretches as far north as Mexico. It was for many years considered to be no more than a section of **Catasetum** by botanists. It differs, however, in having bisexual flowers.*

Scutacaria stelii Lindl.
Amazonas, Rio Negro
May, 1972

Margaret Mee

60. *GALEANDRA DIVES* (*family Orchidaceae*) *Above*

Painting completed in June 1985; plant from Lago Caipuru, Rio Trombetas, Pará.

59. *GALEANDRA DEVONIANA* (*family Orchidaceae*) *Above*

Painting completed in June 1984; plant from the Lago Sapuacá, Oriximiná, Rio Trombetas, Pará.

  Discovered by the famous explorer Sir Robert Schomburgk, who made important explorations of Guyana in the last century for the Royal Geographical Society. He collected it near Barcelos on the Rio Negro.

58. *SCUTICARIA STEELII* (*family Orchidaceae*) *Opposite left*

Painting completed in May 1972, published in Mee (1980); plant from the Rio Negro, Amazonas.

  This species occurs in Amazonian Brazil, the Guianas and Venezuela.

*Margaret's plant is growing on a Jará palm (**Leopoldinia pulchra**) in igapó forest. The orchid's curious hanging leaves may reach to a metre long or more. It is named after Matthew Steele, who first brought it to Europe from Guyana over 150 years ago.*

INDEX

REFERENCES

Bechtel, H., P. Cribb & E. Launert (1981). The manual of cultivated orchid species, Blandford Press, Poole.

Bown, D. (1988). Aroids — plants of the *Arum* family, Century Hutchinson, London.

Freitas da Silva, M., P.L. Braga Lisbôa & R.C. Lobato Lisbôa (1977). Nomes vulgares de plantas amazônicas, Manaus.

Mabberley, D.J. (1987). The plant-book. C.U.P., Cambridge.

Mee, M. (1968). Flowers of the Brazilian Forest. The Tryon Gallery, London.

Mee, M. (1980). Flores do Amazonas — Flowers of the Amazon, Record, Rio de Janeiro.

Mee, M. (1988). Margaret Mee — in search of flowers of the Amazon Forest. Edited by T. Morrison, Nonesuch Expeditions, Woodbridge.

Pabst, G.F.J. & F. Dungs (1975–1977). Orchidaceae Brasilienses, 2 vols., Brücke-Verlag, Kurt Schmersow, Hildesheim.

Pio Corrêa, M. (1984). Dicionário das plantas uteis do Brasil, 6 vols., IBDF, Rio de Janeiro.

Prance, G.T. & T.E. Lovejoy (1985). Amazonia (Key Environments series), Pergamon Press and IUCN, Oxford.

Prance, G.T. & S.A. Mori (1979). Flora Neotropica, Monograph 21(1), New York.

Smith, L.B. & R.J. Downs (1974–79). Flora Neotropica, Monograph 14(1–3), New York.

Smith, L.B. & M. Mee (1969). The bromeliads, Barnes & Co., S. Brunswick.

Spruce, R. (1970). Notes of a botanist on the Amazon and Andes. 2 vols., Johnson Reprint Corporation, New York.

Uhl, N.W. & J. Dransfield (1987). Genera Palmarum, L.H. Bailey Hortorium and International Palm Society, Allen Press, Lawrence.

ACKNOWLEDGEMENTS

The help of the following botanists is gratefully acknowledged:—

Phillip Cribb, John Dransfield, Raymond Harley, Charles Jeffrey, Gwilym Lewis, James Luteyn, Bassett Maguire, Terry Pennington, Ghillean Prance, Brian Stannard.

Thanks are also due to Brinsley Burbidge for the use of photographs.

It is a pleasure to acknowledge the help of Tony and Marion Morrison for freely making available to us the fruits of their own research.

Book design by John Stone;
Photography of Paintings by Milan Svanderlik & Andrew McRobb;
Information and Exhibitions Division, RBG Kew.

Typesetting by Christine Beard & Brenda Carey;
Administration Division, RBG Kew.